Gotland House

CW00348960

ELIZABETH LAIRD

Sugar and Candy

MACMILLAN
ORIGINALS

Sugar is sweet. Sugar is pretty.
Sugar has nice clothes and nice hair.
People like Sugar.

Sugar is happy. She likes her nice clothes and her nice hair. She likes her friends. She likes presents. She likes cookies and flowers and smart boys.

Then Candy comes to town. Candy is sweet. Candy is pretty. Candy has beautiful hair and new clothes. Candy has money and roller-skates and a stereo. People like Candy.

Candy takes the apple and the flowers.
Candy smiles. 'Oh, thank you,' Candy
says. She has a sweet, pretty voice.

5

Sugar doesn't have a stereo. She doesn't have roller-skates. Sugar doesn't like Candy. She doesn't like Candy's clothes. She doesn't like Candy's hair. She doesn't like Candy's sweet, pretty voice. Sugar calls to her friends.

Come to the drugstore with me! Susie? Billy? Joe? Come and buy some ice-cream, or a hot-dog, or a drink.

Sugar's face is red. She isn't pretty now. Her friends laugh and go away. They go away with Candy.

Sugar is very unhappy. She cries. Then Sugar hears something. She looks up. She sees Foss and Tiger. She doesn't like them. Foss and Tiger are always making trouble.

Foss is holding a little boy.

Give me your money.

I don't have any money! Stop, you're hurting me!

The little boy is crying. Sugar wants to help the little boy.

Hey! Stop that! Don't hurt that little boy!

Foss and Tiger look at Sugar. They laugh at her. She is frightened. Foss and Tiger are big and tough. But Sugar wants to help the little boy. She runs up to Foss and Tiger.

Don't hit him! You're big. He's little. Don't hurt him. He doesn't have any money!

Go away and play, little girl.

Sugar does not go away. She puts her arm round the little boy. Foss and Tiger are angry now. Sugar is very frightened. The little boy holds her hand. Sugar puts two fingers in her mouth and whistles.

Foss takes Sugar's arm. He pushes her.
Sugar falls down. Her nice clothes are
dirty now. She shouts
to the little boy.

Quick, kid! Run! Go
and get my friends!

The little boy runs away. Foss and Tiger cannot catch him.

Come on, Foss! Let's get out of here! Her friends are coming!

Sugar's friends run up to her. Sugar stands up. She is not pretty now. Her face is dirty. There is a hole in her jeans.

The little boy talks to Sugar's friends.

Sugar's kind. Sugar's brave. Sugar's not frightened of Foss and Tiger. Sugar's a great girl!

15

Sugar's friends laugh and smile. They forget Candy. They forget Candy's pretty clothes and her roller-skates and her stereo. Sugar's brave and kind. They want Sugar now.

Sugar smiles. Then she sees Candy. Candy is alone. Candy is unhappy.

Come on, Candy. Come and have some ice-cream with us.